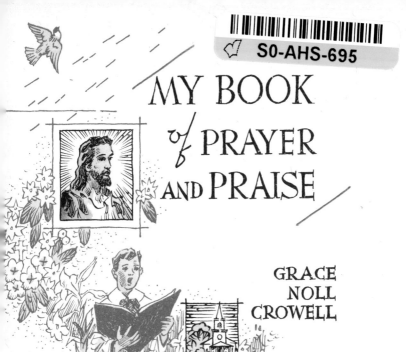

MY BOOK of PRAYER AND PRAISE

GRACE
NOLL
CROWELL

ISHING HOUSE · *Minneapolis*

MY BOOK OF PRAYER AND PRAISE

Copyright 1955
Augsburg Publishing House

Library of Congress Catalog Card Number: 55-7116

Printed and manufactured in the United States of America
by Augsburg Publishing House, Minneapolis 15, Minnesota

illustrated
by LEE MERO

Published by · A U G S B U R G P U

Dedication

This book is affectionately dedicated to all children who love the heavenly Father and who are ever mindful of the beauty which He creates for their daily happiness.

Heavenly Father, bless this book,
May each child who reads it see
That the happiest way to live
Is by keeping close to Thee.

Contents

A GLAD PRAYER

Dear Lord, I kneel beside my bed
That is so soft and neatly spread.
I thank You for it—Oh, there are
So many things to thank You for!
I am as glad as glad can be
For all the things You do for me,
Please know it, Lord, although I may
Not know quite how or what to say,
And keep on blessing me, and make
All children glad, for Jesus' sake.

Amen

HELP ME TO BE GOOD

Every night I climb the stairs,
Every night I say my prayers,
And I pray as each child should:
"Dear Lord, help me to be good."
I do not think that I could pray
A better prayer, and so I say
It over often, and I know
God hears me and He helps me go
Into the new bright day, you see,
For I am good as I can be:
I mind my mother, and I do
The errands that she tells me to,
I do not quarrel, and I find
Many ways of being kind.
And so each night as I kneel there
I know I help God answer prayer.

A BOY'S PRAYER

I am just a boy, dear Lord,
But I offer You my praise
For the light that shines from out
    Your Word,
For the blessing of the days.

I thank You for our daily bread,
I thank You for Your care,
May hungry children, Lord, be fed,
In all lands everywhere.

That we may grow up strong and straight
And be quite brave to face
The tasks ahead, that we may make
This world a better place.

3

BREAKFAST GRACE

Dear Lord, we thank You for the light
After the long good sleep at night.
We thank You for this food, and pray
That You will bless us through the day.
Please keep us brave and true and strong
And kind and helpful all day long.

LUNCHEON GRACE

This is the golden hour of noon—
Above our plate, our bowl, our spoon,
We thank You, Lord, for milk and bread
That strengthens us for hours ahead.
These are Your gifts, dear Lord, and we
Would thank You for them gratefully.

DINNER GRACE

We are so thankful for this day
That has gone on its shining way.
Father, we ask a blessing now
As above this evening meal we bow.
We would be gentle, kind and good
To prove to You our gratitude.

5

PRAYER AT BEDTIME

I kneel beside my bed to say
My prayers, dear Lord, tonight.
I thank You for the good bright day,
And for the star's clear light.
I thank You for my little bed
Turned back so smooth and white.

I am so glad for Your good care
You have been kind and true.
Lord, bless all children everywhere
Who have the need of You.
Watch over every child asleep,
The whole long night time through.

6

THE PICTURED CHRIST

A picture hangs upon our wall:
The picture that I love the best.
From a bright frame the Christ looks down
Upon us, and He is our Guest.

And we are careful what we do,
And we are careful what we say,
We would not hurt the loving Christ
In any shameful, harmful way.

And often as I look at Him
His eyes are smiling, and I know
That He is glad to live with us:
A family that loves Him so!

A CHILD'S WISH

I wish so much that I had lived
Beside the garden wall
That Easter day when Christ arose
And stood so straight and tall
Beside His tomb, and that I could
Have run on swift glad shoes
To tell the other children there
The strange and happy news.

I think we would have tip-toed in
The garden gate to see
The risen Christ—we would have watched
Behind some vine or tree,
And oh, perhaps He would have seen
Us there when daylight came;
Perhaps He would have bid us come,
And called each child by name.

MORNING WALK

When I go out to take a walk
I see so many things:
I see the sunlight shining through
A butterfly's bright wings,
I try to whistle like the bird
That dips and flies and sings.

When I go out to take a walk
I watch the clouds ride by.
They look like old time sailing ships
Against the clear blue sky.
I like to notice how each tree
Has climbed so very high.
It must be God thinks much of me
To make such things for me to see.

THE HUMMING-BIRD

A sudden wind is stirring
And a bird with gauzy wings
Sets his propeller whirring
In a thousand misty rings.

A tiny jet plane shooting
Like an arrow from a bow,
Its destiny, the looting
Of our cypress vines, I know.

Its aviator shedding
All hindering earthly bars,
Splits the air in heading
For those honey-laden stars.

MUSIC BOXES

The tiny music boxes
In the throats of little birds
Send out such happy, joyous
Songs that have no words.

They must wind up those boxes
And set them whirling there
To spin their lovely music
Like silver on the air.

One bird is so delighted,
Up in that leafy tree,
I must run out and thank him
For the song he sings for me.

IF A BIRD IS GLAD

I saw a little gray bird today
Drink at our bird bath on the lawn,
It lifted its head as if to pray,
Then fluttered its gay wings and flew on.

If a bird thanks God for its food and drink,
And if it takes time to look at the sky,
And is glad for its water and food, I think
That surely so should I
Be glad and grateful, and stop to pray
Awhile before running out-doors to play.

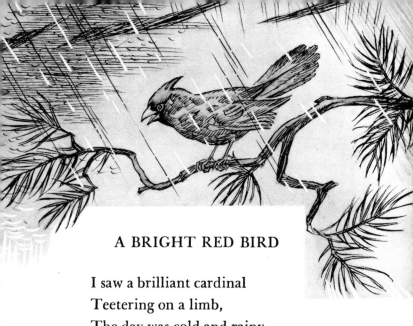

A BRIGHT RED BIRD

I saw a brilliant cardinal
Teetering on a limb,
The day was cold and rainy,
And I was glad for him.

He was like a small lamp
Burning in the night,
He was like our hearth fire
Glowing red and bright.

I think that God was kind, indeed,
To light that lamp for me,
To set a fire on a bough
To glow so cheerily.

THE SILVER LILIES

Last night I went with Rover
Out to the pasture bars,
And in a trough of water
Were three small silver stars,
As clear and white and lovely
As the ones up in the sky.
They looked like water lilies
Upon the lake, and I
Reached my hand down slowly
And made it into a cup,
And slipped it gently under
A star to pick it up.
But the silver petals shattered,
And all the bright drops spilled
Out of my hand, then strangely
After the water stilled,
There were the silver lilies
Each on an unseen stem,
As perfect as if I had not
Reached and shattered them.

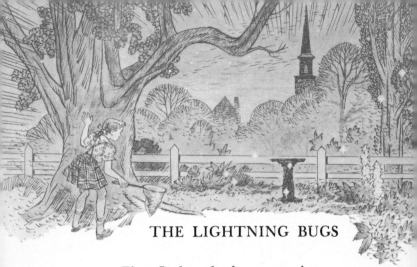

THE LIGHTNING BUGS

First God made the mountains,
Then He made the seas,
Then I think He took a while
To make a thing to please
The little children of the earth:
He made a tiny light
And gave it to a small brown bug
To light its way at night.
And he can turn it on and off—
A pretty golden spark
That flits across the grass at night
Out in the summer dark.
Oh, God was very good to make
The lightning bugs for children's sake.

THE HIDDEN FLOWER

I found a little roadside flower
Quite hidden in the grass—
I stooped to touch it for it was
Too beautiful to pass.

I looked deep in its petaled heart,
So intricately made,
A little unseen flower that grew
Down in the grassy shade.

'Tis strange that God should take
    such pains
With a thing that none might see,
And then I thanked Him, for I think
He made it just for me.

MY BOOKS

I am very glad for all my books:
I open up a cover there,
And suddenly I start away
Upon the road to Everywhere.
Perhaps it is some mountain path,
Or some bright valley where I roam,
Or it may be across the sea,
Where other children have their home.

How strange it is that I can sit
Deep in our puffy old arm chair,
And go so far away that I
Forget that I am sitting there!
In one small book I may become
A beggar maid, or I can be
A lovely queen because she gives
Her throne and jewels all to me.

When mother calls, "I need you, dear,"
I close the book and blink, and blink—
I scarcely know just where I am
It takes me quite a while to think.

ALL GOD'S CREATURES

All God's creatures are beloved by Him:
The little birds, the small squirrels in the
    wood,
The scampering field mice, and the
    scurrying ants,
He sees, and calls them good.

Because God loves the little shy wild things
That He created here beneath the sun,
I shall be careful going on my way
Never to harm one.

BABY MOSES

A Princess went down to the river
To bathe one far-off day.
As she parted the reeds and the rushes
She saw that a baby lay
In a woven wickery basket
That was snug as snug could be,
And there was the baby Moses
Sleeping peacefully.

And there was the watching sister
Who ran through the wind and sun
To bring the waiting mother
To care for her little one.
Oh, wasn't God good to the Princess,
And good to the mother, too,
And very good to Moses
Who served Him his lifetime through!

BIBLE SCHOOL

I like to go to Bible School
When our other school is out,
There are so many wonder-things
That we can learn about:
We play new games, we learn new things,
But always to the end
We learn of Jesus and we come
To know He is our friend.

We learn what He would have us say,
We learn what we should do,
We are taught to think of others first
Our whole long lifetime through.
Sometimes while sitting in my chair
It almost seems that He is there.

JESUS LOVES ALL CHILDREN

Jesus loves all children,
I am certain that He does,
For once He called them to Him,
And I am sure He was
As gentle as a mother
As He touched their face, their hands,
Oh, I am very certain
That Jesus understands
When we are ill or tired,
Or troubled or distressed,
That He can do the same now
As that day when He blessed
The little children whom He bade
Come unto Him, and oh,
I believe if I could run to Him,
I believe if I could go,
He would place His hands upon my head,
And He would stoop and say:
"I bless you, Child, just as I blest
Those others that far day."

THANKSGIVING

It is good our land has set
A day aside lest we forget
To thank God for the sun and rain
And for the harvest's golden grain.

And though I am so very small,
I, too, can thank the Lord for all
His blessings, and I pray He may
Bless every one this special day.

LITTLE PILGRIM CHILDREN

Prudence and Susan and little Jon
Within the stockade square,
Learned their lessons and played their
  games
Happily, gladly there,
And when their parents planned a day
For the giving of thanks, they stood
And crossed their hands and bowed their
  heads
And thanked God as they should.

They thanked Him for the venison,
For the maize that made their bread,
For the purple clusters of wild grapes,
And for apples crisp and red,
And God was pleased and smiled upon
Prudence and Susan and little Jon.

THE GOOD SHEPHERD

Once there was a small lost lamb
That wandered out of sight
From where the other sheep were kept
Safe sheltered from the night;
But the shepherd missed that lamb
And went out through the cold
To find the lost one, and he brought
Him back to the warm fold.

That is what our dear Lord does:
If any child be lost,
He goes to find him, and to bring
Him back at any cost.
Should we not stay so close to Him
That He need never go
To search for us out through the night
Of rain and wind and snow!

LITTLE HOUSE IN NAZARETH

O little house in Nazareth
How pleased Christ must have been
To have your four walls for His home,
Your roof to shelter Him:
The only house He called His home
While He was here upon the earth.
He must have loved your plot of ground,
Your door, your sill, your hearth.

No other house in all the world
Was home to God's dear Son;
No other doorstep waited for
His step when day was done.
From out your door He bore a light
To reach earth's farthest rim—
I know, dear little house, you must
Have meant so much to Him!

THE PLAYMATE

I wish I had been a little child
In Nazareth that far day,
And that Jesus had been a neighbor boy
Who lived across the way.
I think I would have called to Him:
"Come over," and He would
Have run through the bright wind and sun
To play, for He was good
To every child along the street,
And to every one He met,
And the way He played and the words
   He said
One never could forget.
And no one anywhere could find
A playmate that was quite so kind.

LOVING JESUS

I can love my father,
And I can love my mother,
But I can love Jesus
Very much more,
For He gave me my father,
And He gave me my mother,
And He gave me my own house
Roof and wall and door,
Where I am welcome,
Where I am happy,
All these He gave me
Because He loves me so,
And I shall think of Jesus,
And I shall sing about Him,
And I shall tell about Him
Everywhere I go.

HIS BIRTHDAY

Christmas is a child's day,
I am glad that I am young:
Christmas is the loveliest
Song that has been sung;
Christmas is the holiest
Time of all the year,
There are angels singing
For the world to hear.

Christmas Eve is brighter
Than any night, by far,
Illuminated as it is
By the Christ Child's star.
Christmas is the birthday
Of the heavenly King,
Let us make Him happy
By the gifts we bring.

THE SLIP-AWAY

Sometimes when there are girls and boys
And grown-ups for our company
I get so tired of the noise,
I slip away where none can see,
And have the nicest time with me.

I sit as quiet as a mouse,
But really I'm not there at all.
I've gone away from yard and house,
And cluttered room and noisy hall,
And cannot hear my mother call.

And I have such a happy time
Behind that spare-room closet door,
I think up stories, make a rhyme,
Go places I've not gone before,
And I am glad as glad can be
To be there quite alone with me.

I WANT TO BE LIKE JESUS

I want to be like Jesus,
And I shall try to be
As gentle and as patient
And as good and kind as He.
I want to be so like Him
That I, too, can forgive
And love the ones who hurt me,
And oh, I want to live
To please the dear Lord Jesus;
I want to make Him glad.
I would feel very sorry
If I should make Him sad.

My Book of Prayer and Praise contains thirty-one poems for children to use as their very own. It is written by Grace Noll Crowell, author of the book *A Child Kneels to Pray* and other children's books and stories. Lee Mero has designed and illustrated this volume and it is published by Augsburg Publishing House in Minneapolis.